One, Two, Three

Illustrated by Fred Blunt

1 one sun

2 two shoes

3 three keys

4 four doors

5 five hives

6 six chicks

7 seven herons

8

eight gates

9

nine lines

10 ten hens

11

eleven lemons

12

twelve elves

thirteen limousines

14

fourteen fairy queens

15

fifteen submarines

16

sixteen TV screens

seventeen sardines

18

eighteen magazines

19

nineteen jelly beans

20

twenty sentries

Edited by Mairi Mackinnon
Designed by Caroline Spatz

First published in 2011 by Usborne Publishing Ltd., Usborne House,
83-85 Saffron Hill, London EC1N 8RT, England. www.usborne.com
Copyright © 2011 Usborne Publishing Ltd.

USBORNE VERY FIRST READING

There are twenty-four titles in the **Usborne Very First Reading** series, which has been specially developed to help children learn to read.

To find out more about the structure of the series, go to
www.usborne.com/veryfirstreading